SAVAGE BEASTS

Contents

Jack in Africa — page 2

Fierce Animals — page 14

Jan Burchett
and Sara Vogler

Story illustrated by
Martin Aston

Before Reading

In this story

 Jack
 Hippo
 Crocodile
 Lion
 Snake

Tricky words

- fierce
- Africa
- hippos
- crocodiles
- lions
- binoculars
- snakes

Introduce these tricky words and help the reader when they come across them later!

Story starter

Jack was just an ordinary boy but he had a magic backpack. When Jack pulled the cord on his backpack – Pop! – something magic popped out. One day, Jack was reading about fierce animals.

Jack went to Africa.
He wanted to see some hippos.

POP! Out of his backpack came a map.

"There are no hippos here," said Jack.

Jack wanted to see crocodiles.

ZIP! Into his backpack went the map.

POP! Out of his backpack came a boat.

"There are no crocodiles here," said Jack.

Jack wanted to see snakes.

ZIP! Into his backpack went the binoculars.
POP! Out of his backpack came a camera.

"There are no snakes here," said Jack.

"I'll have a sleep now," said Jack.

ZIP! Into his backpack went the camera.
POP! Out of his backpack came a tent.

"There are no fierce animals in Africa," said Jack.

Then Jack saw something.
It looked very big and very fierce.

What has Jack seen?

ZOOM! Jack ran away.

Quiz

Text Detective

- Were there fierce animals in Africa?
- Would you have run away?

Word Detective

- **Phonic Focus:** Initial consonant clusters
  Page 8: What are the two phonemes (sounds) at the beginning of 'snake'? Can you blend them?
- Page 3: Find a word that means 'scary'.
- Page 10: Find a word made from two words.

Super Speller

Read these words:

wanted   sleep   boat

Now try to spell them!

HA! HA! HA!

Q Where do lions buy their clothes?

A At jungle sales.

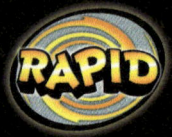

Before Reading

Find out about

- Which animals kill the most people – you might be in for a surprise!

Tricky words

- fierce
- squeeze
- death
- crocodile
- mosquito
- million

Introduce these tricky words and help the reader when they come across them later!

Text starter

There are some very fierce creatures in the world. Snakes, hippos, spiders, lions and crocodiles can all kill humans. But one creature kills more people than any other animal. Which creature do you think kills the most people?

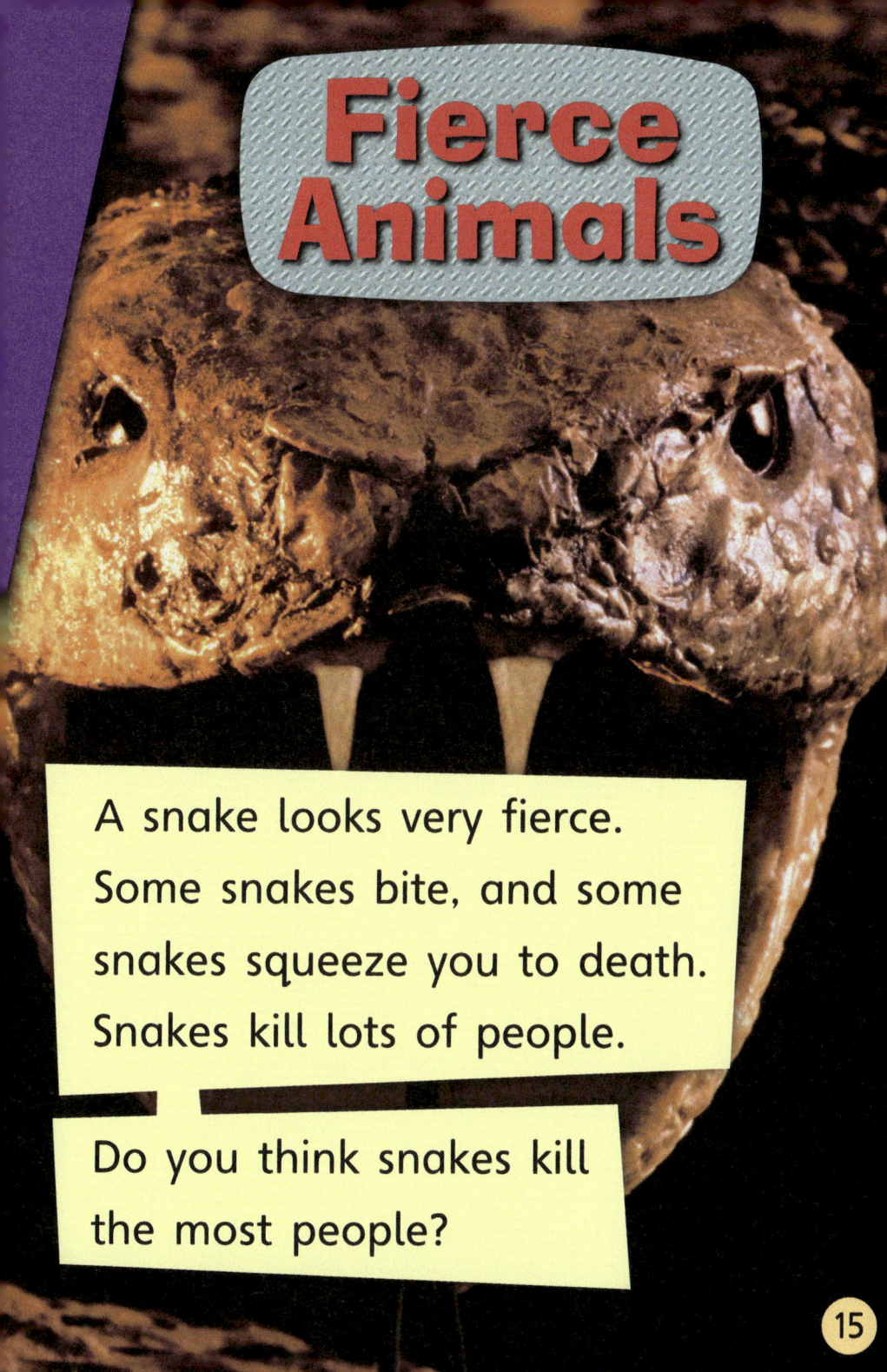

Fierce Animals

A snake looks very fierce. Some snakes bite, and some snakes squeeze you to death. Snakes kill lots of people.

Do you think snakes kill the most people?

A hippo does not look very fierce. It likes to sleep in the mud.

But a hippo can kill people.
It can bite your head off.

Do you think hippos kill
the most people?

Crocodiles kill lots of people.

Do you think crocodiles kill the most people?

A lion looks very fierce.
A lion can kill people.

But lions are very lazy.
They like to sleep all day.

Do you think lions kill the most people?

This spider does not look fierce.

But what do you think of this spider? One bite will kill you.

Do you think spiders kill the most people?

So what kills the most people?
Do you know what it is?

It does not look very fierce.
It is a mosquito.

The mosquito kills the most people.

The mosquito kills three million people a year!

Quiz

Text Detective

- How do snakes kill people?
- Were you surprised that the tiny mosquito is so dangerous?

Word Detective

- **Phonic Focus:** Initial consonant clusters
  Page 21: Sound out the two phonemes (sounds) at the beginning of 'spider'. Can you blend them?
- Page 18: Find a word that rhymes with 'books'.
- Page 18: How many syllables are there in 'crocodile'?

Super Speller

Read these words:

kill   does   bite

Now try to spell them!

HA! HA! HA!

Q What do you call a laughing hippopotamus?

A A happipotamus.